The Prince and the Pauper

Mark Twain

Simplified by D K Swan
and Michael West

LONGMAN

Addison Wesley Longman Limited,
Edinburgh Gate, Harlow,
Essex CM20 2JE, England
and Associated Companies throughout the world.

This simplified edition © Longman Group UK Limited 1987

First published in 1987
Seventeenth impression 1997

ISBN 0-582-52284-6

Set in 12/14 point Linotron 202 Versailles
Printed in China
GCC/17

Acknowledgements

'Photographs © BBC' 1975.

The cover background is a wallpaper design called NUAGE,
courtesy of Osborne and Little plc.

Stage 2: 900 word vocabulary.

Please look under *New words* at the back of this book
for explanations of words outside this stage.

Contents

Introduction

Introduction

Mark Twain

The real name of the writer of this book was Samuel Clemens. He was an American who knew Europe well.

Samuel Clemens was born in Missouri in 1835. He was trained as a printer, but he soon began writing for the newspapers. He loved travel, and he loved the steamboats that went up and down the Mississippi River. He became a steamboat pilot, and the stories he wrote for the papers were often about the people of the steamboats and the river banks. Some of the stories were about real people and places, seen with a keen eye, and told with a love of fun. Some were fiction, like *The Celebrated Jumping Frog of Calaveras County* (1865).

At about this time, Samuel Clemens began to call himself, as a writer, "Mark Twain". The words were one of the calls of the "leadsman" on a river boat. "Mark twain" meant that the line from the boat into the water showed two fathoms (about 3.7 metres) deep, plenty of water for a river steamboat.

In 1867 he went to Europe and the Holy Land with a large group of American tourists. The letters he wrote, collected in a book as *The Innocents Abroad*, are more about the tourists themselves than about the places they visited. America, and later many other countries, laughed joyfully at the tourists and their funny adventures.

Mark Twain's first novel, *Tom Sawyer* (1875), is still widely read and enjoyed. It is perhaps more like a collection of separate adventures than the modern novel, but the reader ends by knowing Tom Sawyer and his friends as if they were real people. One of the friends is Huckleberry Finn, and his name appears again in the title of Mark Twain's most famous novel *Adventures of Huckleberry Finn* (1884).

The Prince and the Pauper (1882) was Mark Twain's first historical novel. It has been made into a film more than once.

The Prince and the Pauper
A few notes about the real history of the time may be helpful to readers.
King Henry VIII died in 1547 at the age of 56. He had been married six times. By his first wife, he had a daughter, *Mary*. By his second wife, he had another daughter, *Elizabeth*. And by his third wife, he had a son, *Edward*, who is the "Prince" of this story.
Edward VI was king for only six years, 1547–53.
Mary followed Edward. She was queen from 1553 to 1558.

Elizabeth I followed her half-sister. She was queen from 1558 to 1603.

London is now a city of 1,580 square kilometres with more than seven million people, but at the time of our story there were about 200,000 people crowded into a city of about 274 hectares. The rich lords had their town houses to the west of the city, between it and Westminster, where the king's palace was.

Chapter 1
Tom Canty

Tom Canty was very poor. He and his family were paupers. There were a great many paupers in London in the year 1547. Sometimes the father of the family couldn't work, and they were paupers for that reason. But Tom Canty's father didn't *want* to work. He and his wife and his mother and his three children all lived in one room in an old house in the poorest part of London. The children had no beds; they slept on the floor.

There were two girls, Bet and Nan, and one boy, Tom. Canty never did any work: every day he sent out his three children to beg for money in the streets. They had to stand at the side of the road and say, "Please give a penny to a poor child!" If they didn't bring money to John Canty in the evening he beat them and gave them no food.

It was a very unhappy life for the children.

Father Andrew lived in the same house. He had a little room at the back of the house. He was a very learned man. Tom went to sit with Father Andrew every day, and Father Andrew told him stories about kings and princes.

Tom said, "I want to be like a prince. I want to speak nicely, as princes do; and I want to learn

Tom Canty and his father

Latin, because princes learn Latin." So Father Andrew taught Tom how to speak nicely and how to be like a prince, and he taught him Latin.

When Tom was with other boys he played at being a prince. Sometimes the boys laughed at him and called him Prince Tom, but they liked him. They played by the river and went swimming in the water. Tom could swim very well.

The King of England at that time was King Henry the Eighth. He had one son, Edward. Prince Edward would be king when his father died.

King Henry the Eighth lived in Westminster Palace in London.

Father Andrew said to Tom: "You should go to Westminster Palace and see a real prince. Prince Edward is the king's son. He lives there, and perhaps one day you would see him."

Chapter 2
How Tom and the prince changed places

So Tom went to the gate of the palace and looked through it. There were two soldiers standing there, one on each side of the gate. They wouldn't let Tom come close. He saw a great many fine gentlemen and ladies coming and going inside, but he did not see the prince. He went to the gate day after day. Then one day he saw a boy coming out of the door of the palace. The boy came quite near to the gate. Tom ran to the gate so as to see him better. "I want to see the prince!" he cried.

One of the soldiers said: "Keep back!" and he hit Tom. He hit him so hard that Tom fell down on the ground.

The prince saw this, and he was angry.

"Why did you hit the poor boy?" he said. "Open the gate, and bring him in."

"He's only a poor beggar boy," said the soldier.

"The king, my father, is king of all the people, rich and poor," said Prince Edward. "Bring the boy in."

So the soldier opened the gate and brought Tom in.

"Come with me," said the prince. "Tell me who you are and why you want to see me so

much. You have come to the gate day after day.
I've seen you from my window."

Then the prince led Tom to a room inside the
palace. He called a servant. "Bring food," he
said.

So the servant brought food and put it on the
table. Tom had never eaten such nice food
before.

"Now," said the prince, "tell me about your-
self. What's your name? Where do you live?"

"I live with my father and mother and grandmother and my two sisters in a room in Pudding
Lane."

"In one room?" said the prince. "Do you all
live in one room?"

"Oh, yes," said Tom.

"There are hundreds of rooms in this palace.
Why do you all live in one room?"

"We're very poor," said Tom. "My father
sends me out to beg for money. If I don't bring
back enough money, he beats me."

"Your father beats you!" cried the prince. "I
shall send my soldiers to beat him!"

"No, no!" said Tom, "That would make my
mother and my sisters unhappy."

"I have two sisters and a cousin," said the
prince. "Lady Elizabeth, and Lady Jane and
Lady Mary. Lady Elizabeth is very wise; Lady
Jane reads books and is very kind. But I don't
like Lady Mary: she never laughs or plays with
me. Do you play with other boys?"

5

The prince with food for Tom

"Yes, of course I do!"

"I don't. What do you play?"

"I play with a ball, and I play by the river, and I swim. And sometimes I play at being a prince."

"I would like to play at being a poor boy like you, and play by the river, and swim. Let's change clothes. Just for a little time you shall be the prince and I'll be the poor beggar boy. Come!"

The prince began to take off his fine clothes, and Tom took off his old clothes and put on the clothes of the prince.

Tom looked at the prince as he stood there dressed in Tom's clothes. He had seen someone very like him before. Where had he seen him? The prince was very like...

"Come and look here!" cried the prince. "Come and look at us in the glass!"

They were just like each other. The prince looked just like Tom, now that he was dressed in the beggar boy's clothes, and Tom looked just like the prince.

"Stay here till I come back," said the prince. He quickly took up a small round heavy thing from the table and put it in a safe place as he ran out of the door.

Tom stood there alone.

Chapter 3
How the prince came to Tom Canty's home

The prince came to the gate of the palace.

"Ho!" he ordered, "open the gate, you men! Quickly!"

The soldiers opened the gates. Then, as Edward passed through, one of them hit him on the head. "That's not the way to speak to one of the king's soldiers!"

The people standing outside the gate laughed as Edward fell on the ground. He got up, and looked at the soldier.

"I am the prince! You shall be killed for that! And you, you fools, you laughed!"

The people laughed again, more than before. Then one of them said: "Bow to the prince! Hats off to our prince! Make way for the prince!" And they laughed as he passed through them.

"He's mad," said one of the soldiers.

"Quite mad," said the other.

Edward went along the street. The people didn't follow him: they were afraid of mad people. Perhaps the boy might be dangerous, they thought.

He walked on and on. He did not know where he was: Prince Edward did not often go out into the streets of London. He was not wearing shoes: Tom Canty didn't have shoes, but his feet were hard. Prince Edward's feet were soon cut by the stones and covered with blood. He was very tired and he needed food.

"Oh, where can I find rest and food?" he cried. "Where can I find someone who will lead me back to the palace?"

A fine gentleman passed by on a horse and Edward called out to him: "Sir! I am the prince. I ask you to take me back to the palace." But the gentleman did not hear what he said; he thought that he was only a beggar boy asking for money, and he rode on.

At last Edward came to a big building that he knew.

"Ah!" he cried. "That's Christ's Hospital. My father the king gave that building as a school for poor boys. I can get help there."

A lot of boys were playing in front of the building. Edward called one of them: "Ho! boy!" he said. "Go to your teacher and tell him to come here. Tell him that Prince Edward orders him to come."

The boy laughed.

"Do as you are told!" Edward said, and he hit the boy.

The boy called out to the others: "Here's a mad boy. His head's hot! Let's throw him into the water!"

Three or four of them took Edward and threw

him into some dirty water and laughed as he climbed out on the other side.

Night was coming on. "It's late," thought Edward. "I must find some place where I can sleep tonight. Then I'll go back to the palace tomorrow. I must go to Tom's house and sleep there... Pudding Lane. That's where he lives."

He went on and on. The sky was red with evening and lights began to shine in the windows of the houses. Then a heavy hand came out of the darkness and took Edward by the arm.

"What are you doing out so late at night? ... Hey?... Tom Canty, can't you answer your father? What money have you got for me?"

"Oh!" cried Edward. "Are you his father?"

"His father? – I'm *your* father!"

"No! No!" cried Edward. "I'm the prince. Your son is in Westminster Palace. Take me there and bring him home."

John Canty looked at the boy. "Mad!" he said. "Quite mad!"

He took the prince's arm and pulled him along. He was a very strong man. "Whether you're mad or not," he said, "you must come home with me, and you shall go out all day tomorrow and bring the money you should have got today."

John Canty

Chapter 4
What happened to Tom in the palace

Tom was alone in the prince's room in Westminster Palace.

He stood in front of the big glass on the wall and looked at his beautiful clothes. Then he walked up and down, still thinking how beautiful he looked. He put his hand on the sword at his side and drew it out. He played at fighting some unseen person with it. Then he sat down and thought: "What a story I'll have to tell my sisters when I get home!"

A bell sounded. One whole hour had passed: the prince was a long time away. "When will he come back?" Tom wondered.

He walked round the room looking at all the beautiful things in it – the finely-made chairs and tables, and the pictures on the walls. There were pictures of kings and princes, of queens and princesses, all in beautiful clothes with jewels, looking down on him with solemn eyes.

There was a suit of armour near the door. Tom stood and looked at it. Then he took one of the arm-pieces and put it on. It was a small suit of armour and it was not too big for him. He took the other arm-piece. A heavy round thing fell out of it. He put on the other pieces and looked at himself in the glass. Then he put everything back as he had found it. He did not know what the round thing was, but he put it back inside the arm-piece.

Another hour! Tom began to feel afraid. "Someone will come and find me here and say: 'Who are you? What are you doing here?' And the prince won't be here to tell them the truth and they won't believe what I say. What shall I do? I must get out of here!"

Then he thought: "Perhaps there is no one in the next room. If I walk quickly and people don't see my face I may reach the gate, and the soldiers will let me out."

So he opened the door. There were four gentlemen standing outside, two on each side of the door. They bowed low.

"Oh! Oh! Oh!" cried Tom and he ran back into the room and shut the door.

The gentlemen looked at each other.

"I think Prince Edward is ill," said one.

"Yes, perhaps he is," said another.

"We should ask one of his sisters or his cousin to go to him," said the third.

"Lady Jane!" said the fourth. "I'll go to Lady Jane."

The door of the prince's room opened. Tom ran back to the far end of the room. He saw a beautiful girl standing at the door. Her face was kind. He fell on his knees.

"What's the matter, my dear cousin?" said Lady Jane. "Why are you on your knees?"

"Save me! Save me!" cried Tom. "I'm not your cousin. I'm not the prince. I'm only a poor boy, Tom Canty of Pudding Lane."

Page 14 (The Prince and the Pauper)
back my clothes!" cried Tom.

"Come," said Lady Jane. "Your father wants to see you."

"My father? Is John Canty here?"

But Lady Jane led him through one great room after another.

One of the gentlemen had told the king that Prince Edward was ill.

Tom was led into a very big room. There was a bed in it, and on the bed he saw a fat man with a white face. King Henry the Eighth was very ill: he had not long to live.

"Come, Edward, tell your father the king: what is the matter?"

"Are you the king?" said Tom.

"Yes, of course I'm the king, and I'm your father. What are you afraid of?"

"Sir, I am not your son! I'm not the prince. I'm poor Tom——"

The king looked at him angrily. "Stop this foolishness! You are the prince, and if you say that you are not the prince, I shall be very angry. And do you know what I do to people when I am

Edward's father, King Henry the Eighth

angry? Do you?"

"Yes, sir," said Tom.

"Now go! Let me hear no more of this foolish talk. You've been reading too many books and they have turned your head. . . .Lord Hertford, go with the prince. He must rest before going to the city banquet tonight. Many great men will be there to meet the prince who will be king when I am dead. Then come back."

Tom was led away to the prince's room. After a short time Lord Hertford came back to King Henry.

"My lord," said the king, "I know that I have not long to live: but the work must be carried on. Orders must be given and laws must be made even when I am too ill to write my name or put my seal on them to make them a law. You must hold the Great Seal and use it for me."

"Yes, Your Majesty. It shall be as you say," said Lord Hertford. "Will you order that the Great Seal should be put in my hands? You gave it to Prince Edward two days ago."

"Yes! I did. Go and ask the prince to give it to you."

Lord Hertford went away and soon came back.

"Your Majesty," he said, "the prince doesn't know where it is."

"He doesn't know where it is? Did he say that?"

"Yes, Your Majesty."

"He can't remember what he did with it!"

"No, Your Majesty."

"He's ill. That's the reason. That's why he can't think."

"Yes, Your Majesty."

"Let it wait," said the king. "He'll remember later, when he is well."

Chapter 5
The royal barge

There were long steps going down from the Palace of Westminster to the river. The royal barge was a big boat in which the king travelled on the river. On each side of the steps soldiers stood waiting for their prince to come out.

The great doors at the top of the steps opened. An order was given and the soldiers stood up very straight. Lord Hertford and other great gentlemen came out and stood on each side. Then they all bowed low as Tom was seen in the doorway. He was dressed in white. He stood there looking down at the river where in happier days he had played and gone swimming: but now he must be a prince. The king had ordered it. He walked slowly down the steps and got into the royal barge.

The royal barge moved out from the side. It moved down the river to the Guildhall – a hall in the city where the banquet was to be.

In the Guildhall all the great and rich men of London sat waiting for their prince to come.

Chapter 6
Edward escapes

John Canty was pulling Edward along to his home in Pudding Lane. People followed laughing at the boy and his father.

"That's right!" cried an old woman. "Teach the boy to do as he is told!"

As they came near the house an old man stepped out. "Let him go!" he cried. "Let the boy go free."

John Canty hit the old man on the head. He fell and lay there. The people passed over him as they followed John.

The old man still lay there: he was dead.

John Canty threw open the door of his room.

"There!" he said to his wife. "There's your son. He hasn't brought home one penny! And he's mad!"

Tom's mother ran to Edward. "Oh, my boy! My poor boy!"

The grandmother laughed. "Your poor boy! Poor useless boy! It's *we* who are poor."

"If you bring home no money, you get no food," said John Canty, throwing Edward down on the floor.

There was a voice outside the door. "John Canty! Quick! Open the door."

"What's the matter?" said Canty.

"I'm your friend Ned. You hit an old man in the street, didn't you?"

"Yes," said Canty. "He tried to take my son away."

"It was Father Andrew – and he's dead. You killed him. You had better get out of here quickly."

"Dead!" said John. Then he turned to his wife and mother. "This is bad! A lot of people saw me hit the old man. They'll tell the judge and I'll be put to death. We must go! Take the girls and meet me at London Bridge. I'll go by another road with the boy."

Canty took Edward by the arm and led him through little streets and dark ways until they came near the river. Then he saw a crowd of people standing and looking out over the river. Some were sitting at tables and drinking. On the banks of the river he saw fires and coloured lights.

"What's all this?" Canty asked a man. "What are you all waiting for?"

"We're waiting to see Prince Edward in the royal barge. He's going to a banquet at the Guildhall. Here, take this, drink it and shout: 'God save Prince Edward!'"

Canty put out his hands to take the large pot of drink. So he let go of Edward's arm. Edward quickly ran away between the men's legs.

Canty looked down. "Where's the boy? Catch him!"

But Edward was lost in the darkness. "To the Guildhall!" he told himself as he ran along the riverside. "There I can find Tom and be myself again."

Chapter 7
At the Guildhall

All the richest and greatest men of the city of London sat at the long tables in the Guildhall. As Tom came into the hall everyone stood up. He took his place at the top table: they sat down.

The banquet began. Servants brought in rich foods and set them on the tables. There was a great deal of talk and laughter. Singers came in and sang, and a company of dancers danced for them.

Edward at last reached the Guildhall. Soldiers were standing at the door, but he cried: "I am Prince Edward! Open the door and let me pass!" The soldiers laughed at him.

"I ordered you to open the door," cried Edward. "Do as I order! At once!"

"Don't be a fool," said one of the soldiers. "Stand back."

But Edward went on shouting at the soldiers. The people in the crowd began to be angry.

"Send the boy away. He's mad." they said. "We want to see the prince come out when the banquet is ended. Go away, boy! Go home!"

"I won't go! I tell you I *am* Prince Edward. I have no friends and no one to help me, but what I say is true."

The crowd began to look dangerous, but Edward wouldn't move. Then a man stepped out and stood by Edward's side.

"I don't know whether you are the prince, or not; I don't care whether you are mad or not; but you're a brave boy and I'll help you."

The man's name was Miles Hendon. He had just come back from the war and was on his way to his house in the country.

The crowd moved nearer. In those days a London crowd could be very dangerous. "Stand back!" cried Miles. The people were now very angry. Miles had to draw his sword. He hit a man with the side of it.

"Kill them!" cried a voice from the back of the crowd. Stones were thrown. A stone hit Edward and he fell. Miles stood over him and fought to keep him safe from the feet of the angry crowd. But there seemed to be little hope. They were so many, and Miles was only one. Miles laughed as he fought.

"Who would have thought that I would live through seven years of war in France and then be killed by a crowd in London!"

There was the sound of horsemen, and a voice cried: "Way! Way for the king's First Lord!" The horsemen drove the crowd away and their leader went into the Guildhall.

Lord Hertford walked up the hall to the place where Tom sat. Then he went down on his knees. "Sir, your father the king is dead." Then he stood up and cried out to the people: "King Henry is dead. Long live King Edward," and all the people in the hall shouted: "Long live our king!"

Miles didn't wait; he quickly led Edward away in the darkness.

Chapter 8
At the inn

As soon as they were safely away from the crowd, Miles began to lead Edward to his inn near the river. As they passed through the streets they heard the sound of shouting behind them. People came running past them. Then the words of the shouting were heard:

"King Henry is dead! Long live King Edward!"

Edward stopped.

"What's the matter?" asked Miles.

"So I am now the king!"

"Prince or king," said Miles, "it's all the same to me. You're a brave boy and I'll take care of you. Come along to my room near London Bridge and we'll get some food. After that fighting I need a good meal."

Miles had a room in an inn near the bridge. As they came near to the inn, Edward heard a voice that he knew too well!

"So you have come at last," said John Canty. "I'll give you a good beating for keeping me waiting so long." He put out a hand to take Edward's arm.

Miles Hendon put Edward behind him and stood face to face with Canty.

"Who are you?" he said, "and what is

this boy to you?"

"He's my son."

"That's not true!" cried Edward.

"Do you want to go to this man?" said Miles.

"No! No! No!" cried Edward. "He isn't my father. I'll die before I go to him."

"Then you shall not go to him," said Miles.

"But I say that he will!" cried Canty, and put out his hand again.

Miles put his hand to his sword. "If you come any nearer I shall put this sword through your body! Now go! Let me see no more of you! Go!"

Canty moved away and was lost in the crowd.

Miles led Edward to a little inn, and went up to a small room at the back. There was a bed, two chairs and a table and a wash-place.

Edward threw himself down on the bed.

"Call me when the meal is ready," he said.

Miles laughed. "Yes, prince," he said. "Have a sleep and I'll order your servants to make ready a banquet."

He went down to the kitchen and brought food up to the room. He put the food down and set the two chairs at the side of the table.

"Your banquet is ready, prince," he said.

"I thank you."

"Come then, and eat," said Miles.

"I must wash my hands first," said Edward.

He washed, then sat down at the table. Miles was just going to sit down, when Edward stop-

Miles Hendon and Edward

27

ped him: "Wait! Don't you know that you must stand until your king gives you the order to sit down? – Now you may sit."

Miles sat down and they began to eat.

"Tell me who you are," said Edward.

"I'm Miles Hendon, and I used to live at Hendon Hall. I was going to marry Lady Edith. But my younger brother, Arthur, told untrue stories to my father about me, and I was sent away to fight in the war. I've been out of England for seven years, and I'm afraid that my brother may not readily give up my home and my lands after so long a time."

"I shall order your brother to give you back your land, and as king I shall add more to it," said Edward. "You have served your king well. Give me your sword. Go down on your knees... Rise, *Sir* Miles Hendon!"

Miles did as he was told. When he stood up again he laughed and said: "So now I am Sir Miles!"

"You are Sir Miles Hendon," said Edward. "I have made you one of my own men."

When they had eaten, Edward fell asleep with his head on the table. Miles took him up and put him on the bed.

"Poor boy!" he said. "He needs sleep. After a long sleep perhaps he'll be well again and stop thinking he is a prince or king, but be himself again."

Miles slept on the floor.

When morning came, Miles woke up. He looked at the boy sleeping on the bed and saw how bad his clothes were. The schoolboys had thrown Edward into the dirty water and the crowd at the Guildhall had nearly pulled them off his body.

"I must go and buy some clothes for my prince," he said, and went out.

One hour later Miles came back carrying the clothes that he had bought. He opened the door of his room and looked at the bed.

Edward was not there!

Miles ran down and asked the servant of the inn: "Where's the boy?"

"A young man named Hugo came to the inn and said: 'Tell the boy to meet Miles Hendon at Southwark Bridge'; and the boy went."

"That man!" Miles thought. "That man who said that the boy is his son! He sent the young man!"

Miles gathered his things together, paid the inn, and set out to find the boy.

Chapter 9
In Westminster Palace

Tom was in bed in Westminster Palace. It was morning. Two gentlemen stood by the side of the prince's bed.

"Your Majesty!" said the first gentleman.

"It is eight o'clock, Your Majesty," said the second gentleman.

At first Tom thought that he was in the room in Pudding Lane and that his mother was calling him to get up. Then he opened his eyes and saw the two gentlemen standing by the side of his bed.

"Your Majesty."

"What?" said Tom.

"Does Your Majesty wish to rise?"

"Do you mean: 'Do I want to get up?'"

"Yes, Your Majesty."

"Yes," said Tom. "I do. Bring my clothes."

One gentleman brought Tom's underclothes into the room and gave them to a second gentleman, and the second gentleman gave them to a third gentleman and the third gentleman helped Tom to get into his underclothes. Then the first gentleman brought his shirt and gave it to the second gentleman and the second gentleman gave it to the third gentleman and the third gentleman put the shirt on Tom. And this was done with each thing.

Tom in the prince's clothes

Tom went into another room to have his breakfast. One servant brought the food into the room and gave it to a second servant, and the second servant gave it to a third servant, and the third servant put it on the table.

A fourth servant and a fifth servant just stood behind Tom's chair and did nothing.

After breakfast a gentleman came and said, "Lord Hertford wishes to speak with the king."

Then Lord Hertford asked if His Majesty was ready to go to the Council Chamber – a big room where meetings were held.

Tom sat in a high chair covered with gold at the end of the room. Men came and bowed, and kissed his hand and read from long pieces of paper. This went on for hour after hour.

"When will this end?" he thought. "I wish I could go and play ball or go for a swim in the river!"

At last Tom learnt that it was time for dinner. He went into another great hall. It was nearly as big as the Guildhall and there were as many servants. Tom thought that the dinner would never end!

"After this," he thought. "I can go and play or swim." But after dinner he had to go and write *"Edward"* on one paper after another. He didn't know what was written in the papers and he didn't care. He saw how the real Edward had written his name and he made his writing just the same.

In the evening there was another great dinner.

When at last Tom went to bed he said to himself: "The clothes are beautiful and it's a beautiful house, and the food is nice, but I don't like being king. I wish I could go back to Pudding Lane and play with the other boys and swim in the river."

Chapter 10
Thief! Thief!

Edward looked at the young man: he didn't like him. He was dirty and his eyes looked from side to side, never straight at Edward.

"Who sent you?"

"Miles Hendon."

"What is your name?"

"My name is Hugo."

"What did Sir Miles say?"

"He said. 'Tell the boy to come to me.'"

"Tell!" Edward was surprised and rather angry. "I am his king."

"He is wounded. He asks you to come and help him."

"Ah," said Edward. "Then I'll go. He is my true servant and I will help him."

The young man led Edward out into the country. They went on, and on, and on.

"Where is Sir Miles?" said Edward.

"Not far from here," said the young man. "He's there in that wood."

They went into the wood. There was a hut in the wood, hidden among the trees.

Hugo opened the door and Edward went in.

"So you have come at last!" said John Canty. "You have come to help your dear father who is hiding here because he killed a foolish old man."

"Where is Sir Miles?" said Edward. "Take me to him."

"I don't know where your friend is, but you seemed to love him so much that I told Hugo to use his name. Now you'll go out with Hugo and get money and food for your dear father. You know how to beg, and Hugo will see that you don't run away."

Hugo led Edward out into the road on the other side of the wood.

"Stand here!" he said. "I'm your brother and I'm very ill. Soon someone will come along the road. I'll cry out in pain and you'll go to him, and say, 'My poor brother! He's ill and we haven't had any food. Help us.' . . . There! There's someone coming."

Hugo threw himself down at the side of the road and began to cry out "Ah! Ah! Ah! I'm dying! . . . Water! Help!"

The man came to him. "Poor boy," he said. "Let me help you."

"Kind sir," said Hugo, "give my brother a penny to go and buy food."

"But you're ill! I can't leave you here in such pain. Your brother will help me to take you to a house."

He turned to Edward. "Come, boy, help me to carry your brother to a house where he can be cared for."

"I'm the king," said Edward. "That isn't my

brother: he's a beggar and a thief. And he isn't ill."

The man looked at Hugo. "Ha!" he said, "another of those beggars! You shall come with me to the judge, and he'll have you beaten or put to death!"

Hugo jumped up and ran away among the trees and the man couldn't follow him.

Edward went on along the road, very glad to be safely away from Hugo. "Now," he said, "I shall never see him or John Canty again." But just then Hugo jumped out on him from the trees at the side of the road.

"So you wanted to have me put to death!" said Hugo. "Don't you know that beggars and thieves are put to death? I'll remember this and teach you a lesson!"

As Hugo walked along by Edward's side he was thinking just what he could do to "teach Edward a lesson".

They came to a town. There were a great many people in the street buying and selling. A woman passed by, carrying a basket. In the basket there was a fine fat hen ready for cooking. Hugo took up a heavy stone from the ground, then he walked along behind the woman. He put the stone in her basket and took out the hen. Then he ran quickly and put the hen in Edward's arms. He shouted: "Thief! Thief!" and went off along the street.

The woman turned. She saw Edward holding her fat hen.

"There's the thief!" she cried. "Constable! Call the constable!"

An angry crowd gathered round Edward. "We won't wait for the constable," said a big man. "There are too many thieves in this place. Let's put an end to him ourselves."

Edward heard the sound of a horse. He looked up and saw Miles Hendon making his way through the crowd.

"Sir Miles!" he cried. "Sir Miles! Help me!"

Miles made his way through the crowd. "So I've found you at last!" he said. "Now what's the matter?"

"That woman says that I stole her hen."

"He took it out of my basket, and there it is!"

"Ah," said Miles, "that's a nice fat bird: just what I ordered you to get for me. But you should have asked the woman if she would sell it."

Miles took the woman's arm and led her to one side. "My servant is rather foolish," he said. "He's a mad boy who thinks that he's the king; so you won't be unkind to him, will you? I am sure he put the money in your basket," said Miles. "Let me look in it." (Miles put his hand inside the basket. He had money ready in his hand.) "Yes! Here it is. Fifty pence. You mustn't say that a boy is a thief until you are sure."

"Here!" said the woman, "take the hen. I

Edward in the town

don't want the money."

But Miles put the money in her basket.

"Come, boy!" he said, and took Edward up on to his horse, and rode away.

"How did you find me?" asked Edward.

"I met a man in an inn. He told me about two beggars. One of them said, 'I am the king and that isn't my brother.' So I knew that one of them was you."

"Where are we going now?"

"To Hendon Hall," said Miles.

"You may take me with you; but after that I must go quickly to be crowned in Westminster."

Chapter 11
Hendon Hall

Miles and Edward spent the night in an inn and went on next day.

In the afternoon they went up a high hill and Miles stopped. He pointed to a big house among the trees. "There!" he said, "that's my home! Have you ever seen such a big house? There are fifty rooms in it and we had twenty servants. Think of that, boy – twenty servants!"

They rode down the hill. "See, here's the church where we went on Sundays. There's the inn. Nothing is changed."

They passed through a big gate. "This is Hendon Hall," said Miles. "How glad I am to be back again! How happy they will all be to see me!"

Miles jumped down from the horse and helped Edward to get down. Then he ran into the house.

A young man was sitting at a table.

"Arthur!" Miles cried. "Say that you are glad to see me again. Where's my father?"

The young man looked up. "Who are you?" he said.

"I'm Miles Hendon, and you are my brother Arthur. I have just come back from the war after seven years."

"My brother Miles was killed in battle three years ago. I had a letter from France saying that he was dead."

"That isn't true! Call my father, Sir Robert! Where is my father? He'll know me."

"Sir Robert is dead."

"Call the servants – those who were here seven years ago. They'll know me."

"They are all new. None of those servants are here now."

"You sent them all away! I see it! You made ready for my home-coming. No one must know me! No one must say, 'That's Miles Hendon.' But Lady Edith will remember me."

"Lady Edith knows that Miles Hendon is dead," said Arthur. "She saw the letter, and she will soon become my wife."

"*You* wrote the letter! *You* told her that I was dead!"

Miles ran across the room at his brother: "You have stolen my home! You have stolen my land; and now you want to steal Lady Edith, who was to be my wife!"

He threw Arthur to the floor.

"Help! Help! Help!" shouted Arthur. The servants heard his cries and ran into the room. They carried Miles and Edward away to the prison.

Chapter 12
Prison

Miles and Edward were in prison.

"How long do you think we shall be here?" asked Edward.

"We shall be kept here in prison until the judge comes. Then he will hear what Arthur has to say and he will give judgement."

"What judgement?" said Edward.

"Perhaps he will think that you and I are both mad and will order us to be beaten and sent away."

"Beat *me*? The king?" said Edward.

They heard a sound at the door. It opened and a man came in. He put some food down on the table. Then, as he turned to go away, he looked at Miles's face, and stopped.

"Basil!" cried Miles. "Basil! You used to work in the garden when my father was alive."

"Why! Yes!" said the man. "It's Mister Miles. No: it can't be. Mr Miles was killed in the war."

"He wasn't killed, Basil. My brother Arthur wrote a letter himself to say that I had been killed because he wanted my land and Lady Edith. Now I have come home."

"Mister Miles, I'm glad to see you again. Your brother Arthur is a bad man. He sent all the old servants away. I'll tell everyone that you are back again."

"No! No!" said Miles. "You mustn't tell any-one that I'm here. If my brother thinks that anyone knows me, he'll send men to kill me when I get out of prison."

"Yes," said Basil. "He would do that."

"When I am set free from here," said Miles, "I shall go to London, where I have friends. Sir Humphrey Marlow is captain of the soldiers at Westminster Palace, and he was with me in France. He knows that I wasn't killed in the war. And there are others. I'll go to them, and they'll go to the king. The king will give me back my home and my land. Say nothing, Basil, till I come here again."

Edward laughed. "The king!" he said. "Ask him who is king now."

"King Henry is dead," said Basil. "Men say that the young Prince Edward is not crowned yet, but he will be crowned soon, and he will be our king."

"We must escape from this prison!" cried Edward. "I must go to London to be crowned."

The judge heard Arthur's story.

"Who is this man?" he asked.

"I don't know," answered Arthur. "How could I know? He is some thief or beggar, and he's mad. He thinks that he's my brother Miles, who was killed in battle three years ago; and I am told that this boy who is with him is quite mad: he thinks that he is the king."

"Let the man be put in the stocks and let the boy be beaten so that he may learn to find better friends."

"No! sir," cried Miles. "The boy is very young and he isn't strong: he's ill. Let me have the beating!"

"It shall be as you ask," said the judge.

So Miles was beaten, and then put in the stocks. People came to look at him and throw things at him, but Edward stood in front. "Keep back!" he cried. "This is my friend. I order you to keep back!"

The people laughed. "He's a brave boy," they said, "and he loves his friend." They threw a few things at Miles – some bad eggs and old fruit – but not very much.

So Miles sat in the stocks all day. In the evening Basil came and brought them food and Miles was set free.

Then Miles and Edward set out to go to London.

Chapter 13
The king is crowned

When Miles and Edward reached London they found the streets full of people. Flags were hanging from all the buildings.

They went to an inn and had a meal. When it was finished, Edward said: "Bring me a pen and paper. I want to write a letter."

"Who will you write to?" asked Miles, laughing. "To the king? He won't read letters today! He's going to be crowned today."

Edward sat thinking with the pen and paper in front of him. "What can I write which will make the great lords believe me? What do I know that Tom can't know – something that no other person in the world knows? ... Yes; there is one thing!"

He wrote a few words. "Now," he said, "let's go to Westminster."

Miles and Edward came to the gate of Westminster Palace. All the great lords and ladies of the country were gathering together in Westminster Abbey – the church in which all the kings and queens of England are crowned. In the Palace of Westminster, Tom was ready to put on the fine clothes in which he would go to Westminster to be crowned. With him were Lord Hertford and Lord Somerset and the rulers of the land. At the door stood Sir Humphrey Marlow waiting to give the order to the soldiers who were to march with the prince to the abbey.

There was a noise at the gate, shouting and sounds of fighting. Sir Humphrey turned to one of his men: "Go and see what is happening."

In a short time the man came back. "There's a man there – and a boy with him. The man says that he is Miles Hendon, and the boy says that he has a letter for the king. I think he's mad. He says that he *is* the king!"

"Miles Hendon!" said Sir Humphrey. "He's a brave man and a good soldier. What is he doing in a fight at the palace gates?"

Tom stepped forward. "Did you say a boy? – with a letter?"

"Yes, Your Majesty."

"Bring them here."

"But, Your Majesty – " said Sir Humphrey.

"I order it! Bring them at once!"

So Miles and Edward were led into the room where Tom and all the great men were gathered.

As Edward came in through the door, Tom ran and threw himself down on his knees.

"Your Majesty!" he cried. "You have come just in time!"

"The madness has come on him again." said Lord Hertford. "What shall we do?"

Edward had raised Tom up, and they stood side by side.

Tom on his knees in front of Edward

47

"Take hold of that boy!" cried Sir Humphrey, pointing to Edward. Then he turned to Miles. "Miles, what are you doing here?"

"Stop!" cried Lord Hertford. "Look at those two faces. They are so like each other, I could almost believe... I don't know what to think. Perhaps our prince here was not mad: perhaps he is *not* the real prince."

"Is there any question that we could ask the boy which would help us?" said Lord Somerset.

Lord Hertford turned to Edward and asked him question after question – about King Henry, about Edward's mother, about the palace and those who worked in it. Edward answered all the questions.

"But," said Lord Somerset, "he might know all those things but not be the real prince."

"What is in that letter?" said Tom.

Lord Hertford took the paper and read:

Where is the Great Seal?

He turned to Tom. "I asked you, Your Majesty, many days ago, but you didn't tell me."

"I don't know what the Great Seal is, and I don't know where it is," said Tom.

Look inside the arm-piece of the suit of

armour in my room," said Edward, "and you'll find it."

"Oh that!" cried Tom. "That round heavy thing! I—"

"What did you do with it?" cried Lord Hertford. "Tell me!"

"I used it to crack nuts."

"He used it to crack nuts!" The great lords and rulers of the land laughed and laughed.

Chapter 14
The end

So the real Edward was crowned king and he was a very good king because he had been among the people and he had learnt how they lived and what they needed. Tom lived in the palace and was the king's best friend.

Sir Miles got his home and his land again and married Lady Edith. King Edward often went and visited him at Hendon Hall, where Basil was working as head gardener.

John Canty was never seen again, but Tom gave his mother and his two sisters a very nice house in the country.

King Edward did not live very long. When he died, Tom went and lived with his mother and sisters, and he wrote this story telling how Tom, the pauper, was for a few days King of England.

Questions

Questions on each chapter

1 Tom Canty
  1 Why was Tom Canty's father a pauper? (Because . . .)
  2 What did the children do to get money?
  3 Who taught Tom Latin?
  4 What was the name of the king?

2 How Tom and the prince changed places
  1 What did the prince tell the soldier to do?
  2 What did the servant bring?
  3 How many sisters did the prince have?
  4 What did the prince take up from the table?

3 How the prince came to Tom Canty's home
  1 Why did the stones hurt Edward's feet? (Because . . .)
  2 What was Christ's Hospital?
  3 What did the boys do to Edward?

4 What happened to Tom in the palace
  1 What was near the door?
  2 What fell out of the arm-piece?
  3 Who were standing outside the door?
  4 What did Tom do when he saw Lady Jane?
  5 Who gave the Great Seal to Prince Edward?

5 The royal barge
  1 What was the royal barge?
  2 Who were waiting at the Guildhall?

6 Edward escapes
  1 What did Canty do to the old man?
  2 What did Canty see on the banks of the river?
  3 What were the people waiting to see?

7 *At the Guildhall*
   1 What did the people do when Tom came into the hall?
   2 What did Edward tell the soldiers to do?
   3 A man came to help Edward. What was his name?
   4 Why did Lord Hertford cry out?

8 *At the inn*
   1 Whose voice did Edward hear?
   2 Who was Arthur? What did he do?
   3 Where did Miles sleep?
   4 What did Miles go out to buy?

9 *In Westminster Palace*
   1 What was the Council Chamber?
   2 What did Tom do after dinner?

10 *Thief! Thief!*
   1 Where was the hut?
   2 "Help me to carry your brother." What was Edward's
     answer?
   3 What did Hugo take from the basket?
   4 Who came through the crowd?

11 *Hendon Hall*
   1 Who was sitting at the table?
   2 What did Arthur say about Miles?
   3 What did Miles do to Arthur?

12 *Prison*
   1 What may the judge order?
   2 Who was Basil?
   3 Who was Sir Humphrey Marlow?
   4 Why must Edward go to London?

13 *The king is crowned*
   1 Where are the kings and queens of England crowned?
   2 What was Tom doing?
   3 What did Tom order Sir Humphrey to do?
   4 What did Tom do when Edward came into the room?
   5 What was written in the letter?
   6 Where was the Great Seal?

14 *The end*
   1 Why was Edward a good king?
   2 Who did Miles marry?
   3 What did Tom give his mother and sisters?
   4 Who wrote this story?

Questions on the whole story

These are harder questions. Read the Introduction and think hard about the questions before you answer them. Some of them ask for your opinion, and there is no fixed answer.

1 Who was the prince's father, and what was the prince to become?

2 What ways of travelling do you read about in this story? Do you know of any other ways of travelling at that time?

3 Why was Tom a pauper?

4 Tom Canty:
   a How old do you think he was in 1547?
   b What reasons do you have for thinking he was that age?
   c There were things that he liked to do, but he couldn't do them when he was the prince. What were they?
   d What happened to him when Edward was king?
   e What happened to him when Edward died?
   f Say whether you think these are TRUE or NOT TRUE:
      1 Tom Canty was a dirty, worthless boy.
      2 He didn't enjoy being a prince.
      3 He wanted to learn and to become a better person.
      4 He was very glad when the real king (Edward) arrived.
      5 He wanted to go on being the king.

5 Prince Edward:
   a How old do you think he was in 1547?
   b What is your reason for thinking he was that age?
   c Why, at the beginning of the story, did he want to change places with Tom?
   d How soon did he wish he hadn't changed places?
   e What happened to him in the end?

   f How was he brave
      1 at Christ's Hospital?
      2 on the river bank when John Canty was drinking?
      3 at the Guildhall?
      4 at Miles Hendon's inn?
      5 in the prison?

6 Miles Hendon:
   a Do you like him? Why?
   b What happens to him at the end of the story?
   c Do you think it is the right ending for him? Why?

7 Do you think Mark Twain wanted you to like one of the boys –
Tom or Edward – more than the other? Can you give a reason
for your opinion?

New words

armour
iron covering for the head and boy in war in old times

banquet
a great meal of fine food

beg
ask for money in the streets; a **beggar** does this

constable
a man who makes people keep the law

crack nuts
break open the hard seeds of certain trees so as to eat the inside part

fiction
writing with the story and people from the writer's imagination

inn
a small house where, for money, you can eat or drink or sleep in a bed

lord
a very important man who comes from a ruling family

pauper
a very poor person

stocks
a place where a law-breaker had to sit with his legs held between pieces of wood while people threw things at him

Your Majesty
words used when you are speaking to a king or queen

Stocks

where prisoners were kept and people threw things at them

fiction

a lie thing,
a story written using your imagination

57